THE MOUSE MARRYING OFF HIS DAUGHTER

老鼠嫁女

编文 剪纸 于平 任凭

英文翻译 喻璠琴

华语教学出版社

北 京

SINOLINGUA

BEIJING

First Edition 1993

ISBN 0—8351—2618—8
ISBN 7—80052—257—1
Copyright 1993 by Sinolingua
Published by Sinolingua
24 Baiwanzhuang Road, Beijing 100037, China
Printed by Beijing Foreign Languages Printing House
Distributed by China International
Book Trading Corporation
35 Chegongzhuang Xilu, P.C. Box 399
Beijing 100044, China

千年佳偶

剪纸艺术

海右乙酉美林

老 鼠 嫁 女

　　"老鼠嫁女"是中国家喻户晓的民间故事。大意是这样的:老鼠一家常年住在阴暗的墙洞里,过着担惊受怕的日子。为了摆脱这种生活,年迈的父母准备为女儿选择一个有权有势的女婿。它们首先想到了太阳,因为太阳照亮四方,万物生长都离不开它,所以便前去说亲。太阳听了以后忙说:"我虽然光照四方,但乌云一来便把我遮住了,我不如乌云,还是去找乌云吧。"老鼠又去找乌云,乌云连连摇头道:"虽然我能挡住太阳的光芒,但大风一吹,就把我吹散了,还是去找大风吧。"老鼠又去找大风,大风说:"我也不行,遇到墙一挡,我就走不通了。"老鼠又去找墙,墙说:"我虽然能挡住大风,但老鼠一打洞我就垮了。"老鼠找了一圈又找到了自己,不过这一圈没有白跑,老鼠从中得到一个启发:太阳怕乌云;乌云怕大风;大风怕墙;墙怕老鼠,那么老鼠最怕谁呢?猛然想到了老鼠的天敌——猫。老鼠全家都为这个高妙的选择而高兴。心想,如果老鼠和猫结了亲,还用怕谁呢!于是,便去向猫提亲,猫一听要做老鼠的新郎,便很爽快地答应了。就这样,老鼠全家忙嫁妆,择定吉日过门。新婚这天,一群老鼠吹吹打打,用花轿抬着新娘进了猫家,新娘一入洞房就没有再出来。到了回门的日子,老鼠父母不见女儿女婿回家,便去猫家探望,猫告诉他们:"因为怕别人欺负新娘,就把她放在肚子里保护起来了。"老鼠父母一听,吓得抱头便跑。

　　"老鼠嫁女"这个有趣的民间故事,虽不见于古籍记载,但在民间却广泛流传。其内容因地而异。有的地方叫《老鼠嫁女》,有的地方叫《老鼠娶亲》。据《延绥镇志》记载:"十日(新正)名老鼠嫁女,是夜家人灭烛早寝,恐惊之也。"这一夜,老人们都催孩子们早上床睡觉,并提醒孩子们把鞋子放好,以防被老鼠偷去做花轿,还要在屋角撒盐和米送给老鼠,俗名"老鼠分钱"。孩子们却总是不肯早睡,都想亲眼看看老鼠娶亲的热烈场面。

　　关于"老鼠嫁女"的"吉日",由于地域风俗不同,时间也不同。苏州卖《老鼠嫁女》年画的人唱道:"年三十夜里闹嘈嘈,老鼠娶亲真热闹。"北京地区则有"十七、十八、耗子成家"的说法。山东高密一带则说"正月初七为老鼠嫁女日"。陕西延绥则为"新正十日"。还有民谣称:"初一场,初二场,初三老鼠娶新娘。"从各地民间传说来看,老鼠嫁女的"吉日",从腊月到正月,差不多有十几个日子。尽管娶亲日期不同,但内容上几乎大同小异,都是把老鼠拟人化,按照人间结婚仪仗进行排列,这在民间木版年画中可以看到。

　　中国木版年画已有上千年历史。据北宋孟元老《东京梦华录》记载,当时年节前的开封市面上多有卖年画的。后来江苏的桃花坞、天津的杨柳青、山东的潍县等逐渐形成为中国印刷出版年画的中心。在各地出版的年画中，几乎都有《老鼠嫁女》的故事。鲁迅先生在回忆童年生活时记述说："我的床前就贴着两张花纸，一是'八戒招赘'满纸长嘴大耳，我以为不甚雅观；别的一张'老鼠成亲'却可爱，自新郎、新娘以至傧相，宾客、执事，没有一个不是尖腮细腿、象煞读书人的，但穿的都是红衫绿裤。"木版年画除了各种鼠形外，还刻有少许文字。山东平度的一幅木版年画上刻的文字是："老鼠本姓强，家住在仓房；择定娶亲日，假伴装新郎"。山东潍县的年画题句是："一伙小老鼠，作怪成了精；猫王心生气，连皮一口吞。"陕西凤翔县年画上的文字为："佳期百日庆回门，胆大老鼠来迎婚；三遇狸猫山后立，一口吞去命归阴。"

民间剪纸表现"老鼠嫁女"的内容，和木版年画一样有着悠久的历史，而且场面宏大，往往有几百甚至上千只老鼠。千姿百态的老鼠各司其职，前呼后拥，浩浩荡荡。完全依据各种民间传说和传统结婚仪式，将老鼠嫁女的宏大场面作以叙述。从鼠打灯笼开始，到鼠官压阵为止，中间内容有：鸣锣开道、旗牌伞扇、锣鼓花轿、骑马伴郎、陪送嫁妆、车队傧相、娘家客人，嫁女队伍过山梁，走小桥，肩抬车运一派繁忙。

在民间"老鼠嫁女"除了用木版年画和剪纸表现以外，还有以泥、布玩具及皮影来表现的。到了现代，"老鼠嫁女"还被搬上了银幕和屏幕。多少年来，"老鼠嫁女"这一民间传说，既包含着人们化灾为吉的传统思想，同时又为儿童的生活增添了无穷的乐趣。

THE MARRIAGE OF MISS MOUSE

The story of *The Marriage of Miss Mouse* is based on "The Mouse Marrying Off His Daughter", a folktale well-known in most Chinese households. The original story is as follows: The aging Mouse lives with his family in a dark, dismal hole in the corner of a wall and leads a frightened and worried life all the year round. The Mouse and his wife, in order to better their life, plan to marry their daughter to someone powerful and influential. They first settle on the Sun, who sheds light on the universe and on whom all things on earth depend for their growth. When they broach the matter to the Sun, he answers: "Although I shed light on the universe, when the Black Cloud comes he obstructs me. The Black Cloud is more powerful than I. You'd better go to him." When the Mouse approaches the Black Cloud, the Black Cloud shakes his head vigorously. "Although I can obstruct the brilliance of the Sun, the Wind always scatters me. You'd better go to him." So the Mouse seeks out the Wind, who replies, "I'm no good. When a Wall blocks my way, I can't go anywhere." Next the Mouse approaches the Wall and is told: "Although I can block the path of the Wind, I am prone to crumble when the Mouse makes holes in me." So the Mouse's excursion brings him back to himself. Nevertheless, the Mouse's efforts are not wasted. He is enlightened by what he has found out: The Sun fears the Cloud, the Cloud fears the Wind, the Wind fears the Wall, the Wall fears the Mouse. Who, then, does the Mouse fear?

The Cat, the Mouse'e natural enemy, suddenly comes to his mind! The entire family is very happy with this wonderful choice. Think of it, if the Mouse were to be linked in marriage with the Cat, then, from that time on, whom would he fear? Therefore, the Mouse approaches the Cat and proposes the Cat marry his daughter. The Cat, upon hearing the proposal of marriage to a Mouse, agrees readily. So the Mouse and his household immediately busy themselves preparing their daughter's dowry and choose an auspicious day for the wedding. On the day of the wedding, a group of mice, preceded by a band, carry the bride in a sedan chair to the Cat's home. Once the bride enters her bridal chamber, the mice never set eyes on her again. Because their daughter and son-in-law do not come calling on the day the bride is supposed to visit her parents, the Mouse and his wife go to visit the young couple. But the Cat tells them, "To protect my wife from possible bullies, I have put her in safekeeping in my stomach." Taken aback, the Mouse and his wife scurry away in fright.

This interesting story, although not recorded in the classics, is extremely popular throughout China. Its title and content differ from place to place. In some areas, it is called "The Mouse Marrying Off His Daughter"; in others, "The Mouse Taking a Wife". According to the "Annals of Yansui Town": "On the tenth day of the first lunar month, the Mouse marries off his daughter. On that night, they holler: "On the seventeenth and the eighteenth of the first lunar month, the Mouse gets married." In the vicinity of Gaomi, Shandong Province, they say: "On the seventh day of the first lunar month, the Mouse marries off his daughter." In Yansui, Shaanxi Province, it is: "On the tenth day of the first lunar month." A folk song puts it this way: "On the first day, on the second day and on the third, the Mouse marries." So the Mouse can have more than ten wedding days between the last month of one lunar year and the first month of the next. The dates may differ, but there are few discrepancies in the contents of the stories. The mice are always anthropomorphized, and the wedding equipage is similar to that of human beings. This can be seen in the wood-block New Year's posters.

Chinese wood-block New Year's posters have a history of over a thousand years. According to the Reminiscences of the Eastern Capital by Meng Yuanlao of the Northern Song Dynasty, in his time numerous New Year's posters were sold in the city of Kaifeng. Later, the Daohuawa area of the city of Suzhou, the Yangliuqing section of the city of Tianjin and Weixian County in Shandong Province gradually developed into publishing centres for New Year's posters. And the story of "The Mouse Marrying Off His Daughter" often appears in these posters. In describing his childhood, Lu Xun wrote, "Two colourful pictures were pasted beside my bed. One was 'Pigsy Marries into His Wife's Family'. I thought the pig's big ears and long snout ugly. The other one, 'The Mouse's Wedding', was quite lovely. The bridegroom and his bride, together with the best men and bridesmaids, guests, and attendants, all had pointed mouths and thin legs. They looked like scholars, but were wearing red tunics and green trousers." On some wood-block New Year's posters, verses are inscribed along with the picture. One poster from Pingdu, Shandong Province, is inscribed as follows: "The Mouse is named Qiang, and he lives in a big granary. He chooses a day to take a wife and is decked out to be the groom." In another poster, made in Weixian County, Shandong Province, the inscription reads: "Naughty are the little mice, as mischievous as little elves. They get the Cat's back up, and he then gobbles them up skin and all." A poster from Fengxiang County, Shaanxi Province, has the following inscription: "A hundred days after the wedding, a brave Mouse comes to welcome his daughter home. Behind a mountain, the Cat waits, and swallows the brave Mouse whole."

Like wood-block New Year's posters, Chinese papercuts also have a long history and depict the same theme—sometimes with hundreds, or even thousands, of mice, each different in posture, assuming various positions in the ceremony. The large wedding equipage, presented according to tradition, begins with mice holding lanterns; mice officials bring up the rear. Those in between beat gongs and hold up banners, tablets, umbrellas and fans. The bride rides in a sedan chair. The best men ride on horseback beside the groom. There are loads of goods for the dowry, carts, bridesmaids, and the family and friends of the bride. The entourage crosses mountain ridges and small bridges. It is a really boisterous scene.

Besides being depicted in wood-block New Year's posters and papercuts, the theme of the Mouse marrying off his daughter also appears in clay and cloth toys and in shadow plays. In recent years, it has even been reproduced on television and movie screens. For many years, besides embodying traditional thought about transforming suffering into good fortune, this folktale has enriched the lives of children.

大红喜字墙上挂，
老鼠女儿要出嫁。

Dà hóng xǐzì qiáng shang
guà,
lǎoshǔ nǚ'er yào chūjià.

The Double Happiness char-
acters are written up in
red.
Young Miss Mouse is about
to be wed.

1

女儿不知嫁给谁，
只得去问爸和妈。

Nǚ'er bùzhī jià gěi shuí,
zhǐdé qù wèn bà hé mā.

But she can't make her mind
up in choosing a spouse,
And leaves the decision to
Mr. and Mrs. Mouse.

2

爸妈都是老糊涂，
争来争去定不下。

Bà mā dōu shì lǎo hútu,
zhēng lái zhēng qù dìng bu
xià.

Both Mr. and Mrs. Mouse
   are advanced in years,
And argue over what's best
   for their daughter dear.

3

父母二人细商量，
选婿要选势力强。

Fùmǔ èr rén xì shāngliang,
xuǎn xù yào xuǎn shìlì
qiáng.

Much discussion Mr. and
Mrs. Mouse go through,
And conclude only the most
powerful and mighty suit-
or will do.

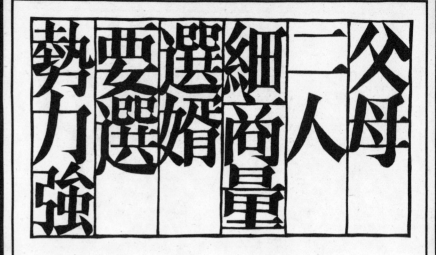

女儿听罢仔细想，
势力最强是太阳。

Nǚ'er tīngbuà zǐxì xiǎng,
shìlì zuì qiáng shì tàiyáng.

Her parents' idea Miss
Mouse mulls in her head,
And decides it is the Sun to
whom she should be wed.

5

女儿前去问太阳，
谁的势力比你强？

Nǚ'er qián qù wèn tàiyáng,
shuí de shìlì bǐ nǐ qiáng?

Approaching the Sun, Miss
  Mouse inquires,
"Is there anyone whose pow-
  er than yours is higher?"

6

太阳说：
乌云能把我遮挡，
它的势力比我强。

Tàiyáng shuō:
Wūyún néng bǎ wǒ zhēdǎng,
tā de shìlì bǐ wǒ qiáng.

The Sun says:
"The Black Cloud obstructs me, as you can see.
It is much stronger and more powerful than me."

7

女儿又去问乌云，
你最怕的是何君？

Nǚ'er yòu qù wèn wūyún,
nǐ zuì pà de shì hé jūn ?

**Then Miss Mouse the Black
  Cloud nears,
"Whom do you most hold in
  fear?"**

乌云说：
大风能把我吹散，
大风来了我胆颤。

Wūyún shuō:
Dàifēng néng bǎ wǒ chuī
sàn,
dàfēng láile wǒ dǎnzhàn.

The Black Cloud says:
"The Wind, which can easily
    blow me away,
I live in fear of it each and
    every day."

9

女儿又去问大风，
谁能和你相竞争？

Nǚ'er yòu qù wèn dàfēng,
shuí néng hé nǐ xiāng
jìngzhēng?

Miss Mouse next the Wind
  seeks out,
And asks, "Is there anyone
  whom you cannot rout?"

10

大风说：
围墙能挡我的路，
我见围墙心打怵。

Dàfēng shuō:
Wéiqiáng néng dǎng wǒ de
lù,
wǒ jiàn wéiqiáng xīn dǎchù.

The Wind says:
"The Wall blocks my path,
  and I can't get 'round.
When I encounter it, my
  heart starts to pound."

11

女儿又去问围墙，
你最害怕那位郎？

Nǚ'er yòu qù wèn wéiqiáng,
nǐ zuì hàipà nǎ wèi láng?

So Miss Mouse goes and asks
  the Wall,
"Who is it that you fear most
  of all?"

12

围墙说：
老鼠打洞我就垮，
见了老鼠我害怕。

Wéiqiáng shuō：
Lǎoshǔ dǎ dòng wǒ jiù kuǎ,
jiànle lǎoshǔ wǒ hàipà.

The Wall says:
"The Mice bore holes and
    down I fall.
They are the ones I fear most
    of all."

13

女儿听罢问自己，
谁是老鼠的天敌？

Nǚ'er tīng bà wèn zìjǐ,
shuí shì lǎoshǔ de tiāndí ?

Then Miss Mouse asks her-
self,
Who's the natural enemy of
the mouse?

14

想来想去猛想起，
鼠的天敌是猫咪。

Xiǎnglái xiǎngqù měng xiǎngqǐ,
shǔ de tiāndí shì māomī.

She thinks and thinks, then
    suddenly sees—
The Cat is the Mouse's worst
    enemy.

15

老鼠最怕大猫咪，
看来猫咪最势力。

Lǎoshǔ zuì pà dà māomī,
kànlái māomī zuì shìlì.

The Mouse fears the Cat
  with its sharp tooth and
  claw,
So the Cat is the most powerful one of all.

16

女儿就去找猫咪，
讲明自己的来意。

Nǚ'er jiù qù zhǎo māomī,
jiǎngmíng zìjǐ de láiyì.

Miss Mouse goes out,
  straight as a bat,
And discusses her intentions
  with the Cat.

17

猫咪听说作新郎，
心里美得喜洋洋。

Māomī   tīngshuō   zuò
xīnláng,
xīn li měi de xǐyángyáng.

The Cat is overjoyed to learn
That he is going to be the
groom.

18

老鼠与猫定吉日，
择定初七为婚期。

Lǎoshǔ yǔ māo dìng jírì.
zédìng chūqī wéi hūnqī.

For their wedding Miss
Mouse and the Cat want
an auspicious date.
So until the seventh of the
following month they
must wait.

初七夜里闹嘈嘈，
老鼠嫁女真热闹。

Chūqī yè li nàocáocáo,
lǎoshǔ jià nǚ zhēn rènào.

The celebration on the seventh is boisterous and
bright.
The wedding procession
lights up the night.

20

鼠打灯笼前开道，
花灯队伍一大套。

Shǔ dǎ dēnglong qián kāidào,
huādēng duìwu yí dà tào.

A festive lantern troop leads the way.
In the darkness, the hand-held lanterns sway.

21

花灯喜灯太阳灯，
大灯小灯亮晶晶。

Huādēng   xǐdēng
tàiyángdéng,
dàdēng   xiǎodēng
liàngjīngjīng.

Sparkling bright, large and
  small lanterns shine,
Decorated with sun and
  flower and Double Happiness designs.

22

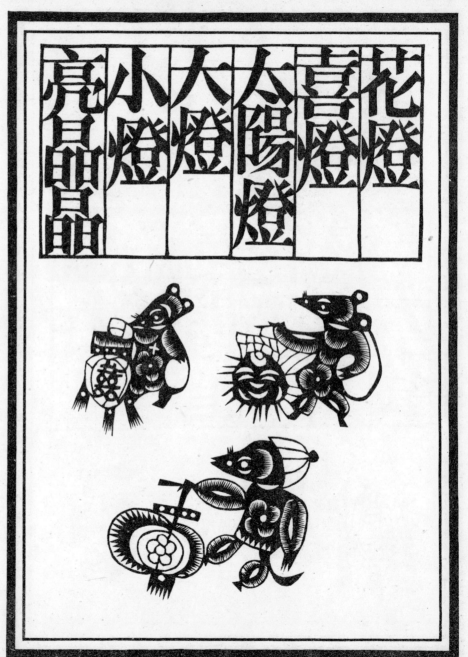

鸡灯羊灯兔子灯，
照前照后忙不停。

Jīdēng yángdēng tùzidēng,
zhào qián zhào hòu máng bu
tíng.

Lanterns in the shape of
sheep, chickens and rab-
bits
Keep the front and the rear
of the troop brightly lit.

猪灯鱼灯月亮灯，
紧走慢跑赶路程。

Zhūdēng　　　　yúdēng
yuèliangdēng，
jǐn　zǒu　màn　pǎo　gǎn
lùchéng。

Lanterns shaped like pigs,
　　fish and the moon
After the others, come along
　　soon.

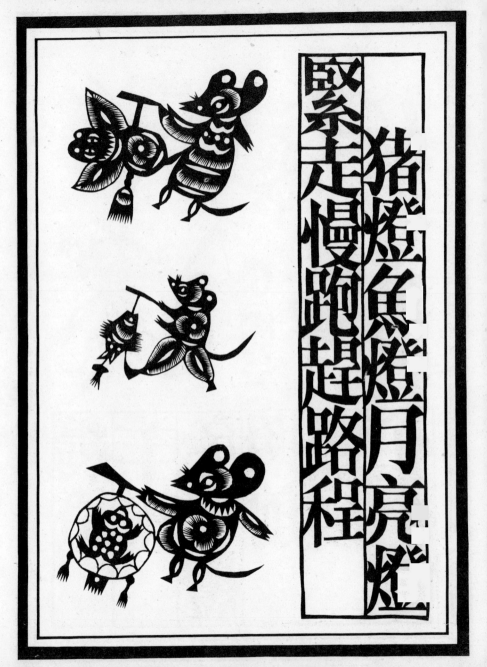

24

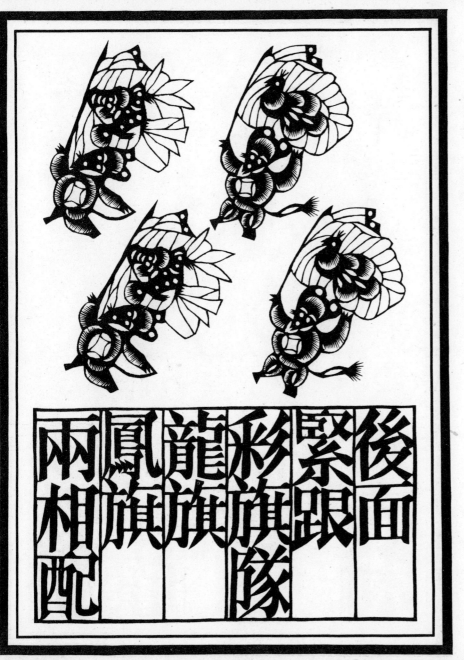

后面紧跟彩旗队，
龙旗凤旗两相配。

Hòumian jǐn gēn cǎiqí duì,
lóngqí fèngqí liǎng xiāngpèi.

And the banner troop follows behind,
With dragon banners for the groom and phoenix banners for the bride.

25

麒麟旗，状元旗，
样样齐全求吉利。

Qílínqí, zhuàngyuánqí,
yàngyàng qíquán qiú jílì.

With unicorn banners and
   the first imperial scholar
   banner,
Each and every to bring happiness and good luck of all
   manner.

旗牌伞扇不可少，
后面乐队更热闹。

Qípái sǎnshàn bùkě shǎo,
hòumiàn yuèduì gèng rènao.

First all the banners, tablets,
  umbrellas and fans,
Then comes the lively wedding band.

喇叭吹，锣鼓敲，
送亲乐队齐来到。

Lǎba chuī, luógǔ qiāo,
sòng qīn yuèduì qí láidào.

Gongs and drums clamour,
trumpets blare,
As the sound of the band fills
the air.

28

大锣鸣，小锣响，
开道铜锣敲得忙。

Dàluó míng, xiǎoluó xiǎng,
kāidào tóngluó qiāo de
máng.

Bronze gongs ring out, large
 and small,
Clearing the way for one and
 all.

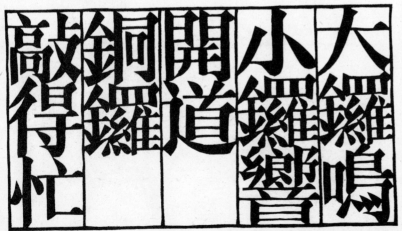

锣声鼓声响一片，
众鼠打鼓更带劲。

Luóshēng gǔshēng xiǎng yí
piàn,
zhòng shǔ dǎ gǔ gèng
dàijìnr.

The Mice strike the drums
  with all their might,
And the din of the music
  spreads through the night.

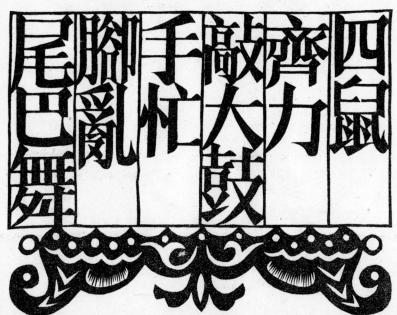

四鼠齐力敲大鼓，
手忙脚乱尾巴舞。

Sì shǔ qí lì qiāo dàgǔ,
shǒumáng jiǎoluàn wěiba
wǔ.

Four mice in unison a big
　　drum beat,
With their tails dancing,
　　their paws as busy as their
　　feet.

31

腰鼓队，打得好，
又打又跳不乱套。

Yāogǔduì dǎ de hǎo,
yòu dǎ yòu tiào bú luàntào.

The waist-drummers put on
   a very good show,
Beating and jumping in for-
   mation, just so.

边打鼓，边吹号，
鼓有声来号有调。

Biān dǎ gǔ，biān chuī hào，
gǔ yǒu shēng lai hào yǒu
diàor.

On one side, the drums
sound out the beat.
On the other, the horns make
the tune complete.

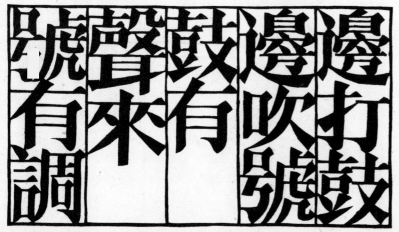

号声悠扬笛声脆，
老鼠自己也陶醉。

Hàoshēng yōuyáng díshēng
cuì,
lǎoshǔ zìjǐ yě táozuì.

Hearing the melodious horns
and the flutes clear and
crisp,
The Mice become enraptured
and filled with bliss.

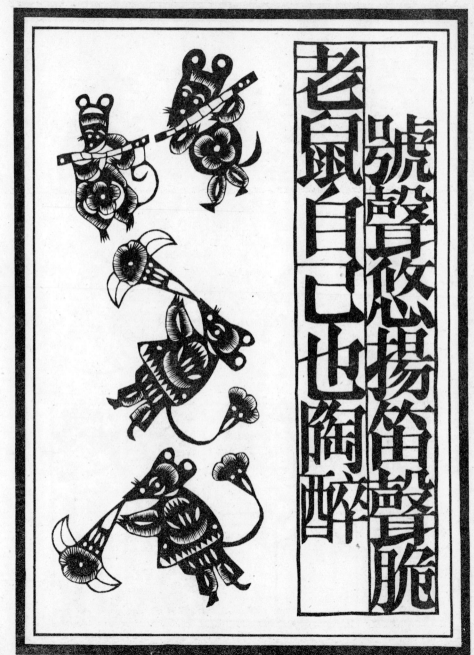

34

吹笙奏乐还唱歌，
边吹边舞乐呵呵。

Chuī shēng zòu yuè hái chànggē,
biān chuī biān wǔ lèhēbē.

Reed pipes accompany the singing of songs,
And to the singing performers dance along.

后面紧跟大喇叭，
众鼠齐声吹唢呐。

Hòumiàn jǐn gēn dà lǎba,
zhòng shǔ qíshēng chuī
suǒnà.

The big trumpets follow,
   close as they should,
And a chorus of Mice blow
   on horns of wood.

呜哇哇，呜哇哇，
唢呐吹得顶呱呱。

Wūwāwā wūwāwā,
suǒnà chuī de dǐngguāguā.

Wu ... wa, wu ... wa, wu
... wa,
Go the wooden horns for all
to hear.

噼哩啪，噼哩啪，
后面鞭炮开了花。

Pīlipā，pīlipā，
hòumiàn biānpào kāile huā.

Pilipa, pilipa, pilipa,
Crack the fireworks in the
rear.

鞭炮迎来大花轿，
轿里新娘咪咪笑。

Biānpào yínglái dà huājiào,
jiào li xīnniáng mīmī xiào.

The fireworks herald the bridal sedan chair,
In which sits Miss Mouse smiling and fair.

轿后紧跟送亲队，
娘家送亲求富贵。

Jiào hòu jǐngēn sòngqīn duì,
niángjia sòngqīn qiú fùguì.

Following the sedan chair
   come the bride's kin,
To wish her great wealth and
   honour as her married life
   begins.

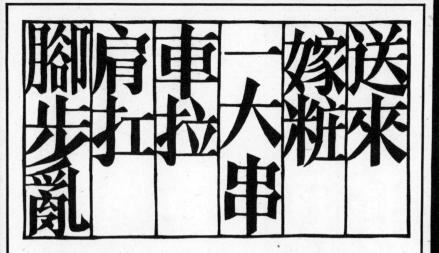

送来嫁妆一大串，
车拉肩扛脚步乱。

Sònglai jiàzhuang yí dà chuàn,
chē lā jiān káng jiǎobù luàn.

They bring a dowry of goods of all kinds.
Some they carry on their shoulders, some on carts they drag behind.

41

什么嫁妆一大串，
请你向后看一看。

Shénme jiàzhuang yí dà chuàn,
qǐng nǐ xiàng hòu kàn yi kàn.

What kinds of goods make up the dowry?
Just take a look and you'll easily see.

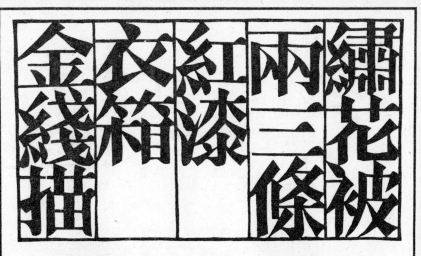

绣花被，两三条，
红漆衣箱金线描。

Xiùhuābèi liǎng sān tiáo,
hóngqī yīxiāng jīnxiàn
miáo.

Two or three quilts of em-
broidery fine,
And lacquered chests with
gold design.

绸缎花布花棉袄，
十年八年穿不了。

Chóuduàn   huābù   huā
mián'ǎo,
shí nián bā nián chuān bu
liǎo.

Enough padded jackets, and
    silk and satin
To last the bride eight years,
    or maybe ten.

44

这边还有瓷花瓶，
车推鼠拉慢慢行。

Zhèbian hái yǒu cí huāpíng,
chē tuī shǔ lā mànmàn
xíng.

Porcelain vases of shape and
    size nice,
Pulling and pushing slowly
    proceed the Mice.

45

那边还有运粮车，
拉来五谷真不少。

Nàbian hái yǒu yùn liáng chē,
lālai wǔgǔ zhēn bu shǎo.

In addition, there are carts
    filled with grain,
Of many varieties, each dif-
    ferent in name.

萝卜连叶都送去，
叶子还能当床铺。

Luóbo lián yè dōu sòngqu,
yèzi háinéng dàng chuáng
pŭ.

They even send turnips with
　　leaves on their heads,
For turnip leaves make very
　　comfortable beds.

还有鲜鱼和白菜，
娘家一齐都送来。

Háiyǒu xiānyú hé báicài,
niángjia yìqí dōu sònglai.

And then there are cabbages
　　and fresh fish.
Nothing does the bride's
　　family miss.

猪头狗肉牛车拉，
吃的东西别落下。

Zhūtóu gǒuròu niúchē lā,
chī de dōngxi bié làxia.

An oxcart is loaded with pigs'
    heads and dog meat.
The Mice don't want to run
    out of things to eat.

別落下 東西 吃的 牛車拉 狗肉 猪頭

送吃送穿还送钱，
后面送来金和银。

Sòng chī sòng chuān hái
sòng qián,
hòumian sònglai jīn hé yín.

Besides food and clothing,
  there is also cash.
Of precious metal the bride's
  family has quite a stash.

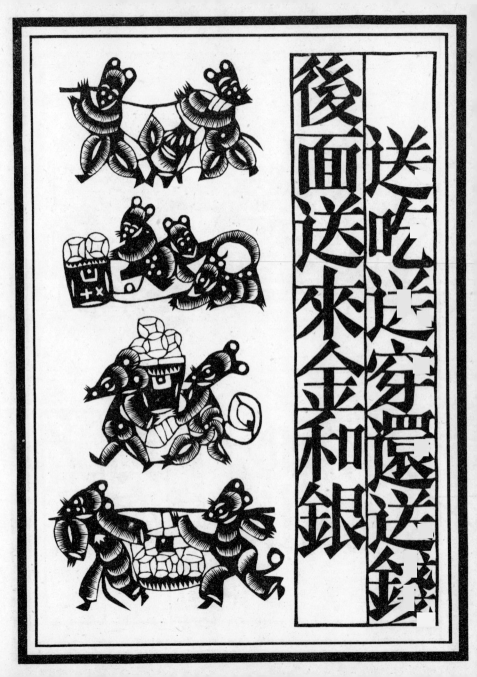

50

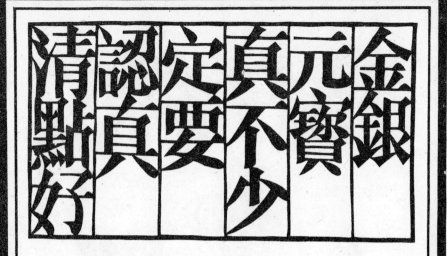

金银元宝真不少,
定要认真清点好。

Jīn yín yuánbǎo zhēn bu shǎo,
dìng yào rènzhēn qīngdiǎn hǎo.

Heaps of ingots silver and
golden—
Better count them carefully,
then hide them so they
won't get stolen.

大石榴，赛金砖，
榴开百子样样全。

Dà shíliu , sài jīnzhuān ,
liú kāi bǎizǐ yàngyàng quán.

Large pomegranates are even
    better than bricks of gold,
For when they burst open
    they reveal seeds in num-
    bers untold.

大枣花生不可少，
早生贵子想周到。

Dàzǎor huāshēng bù kě shǎo,

zǎo shēng guìzǐ xiǎng zhōudào.

Of dates and peanuts, there must be lots,
For they represent the early birth of many tiny tots.

盒子荷花也要有，
和和美美天长久。

Hézi héhuā yě yào yǒu,
héhé měiměi tiān chángjiǔ.

Boxes and lotuses are also a
　　must,
For they symbolize a long
　　life of harmony and trust.

54

扣碗还有交杯酒，
合卺之喜永保留。

Kòuwǎn háiyǒu jiāobēijiǔ,
héjǐn zhī xǐ yǒng bǎoliú.

Lidded teacups and nuptial
  wine
Of blissful wedlock are a
  sign.

茶壶葫芦表吉祥，
多子多孙辈辈强。

Cháhú húlu biǎo jíxiáng,
duō zǐ duō sūn bèibèi qiáng.

Teapots and gourds are most
   auspicious,
Showering generation after
   generation with all sorts of
   good wishes.

56

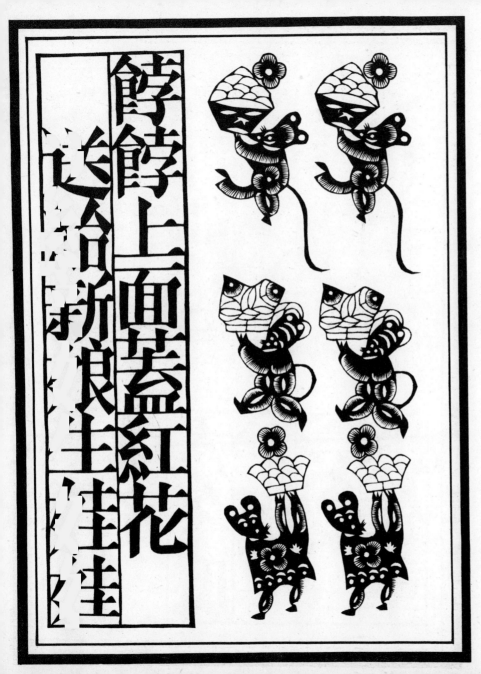

饽饽上面盖红花，
送给新娘生娃娃。

Bōbo shàngmiàn gài hónghuā,
sònggěi xīnniáng shēng wáwa.

Red flowers decorate the tops of white buns,
In hopes that to the bride many children will come.

苹果桃子大冬瓜，
平平安安度年华。

Píngguǒ táozi dà dōngguā,
píngpíng ān'ān dù niánhuá

Winter melons, apples and
    peaches round,
All symbolize a life peaceful
    and sound.

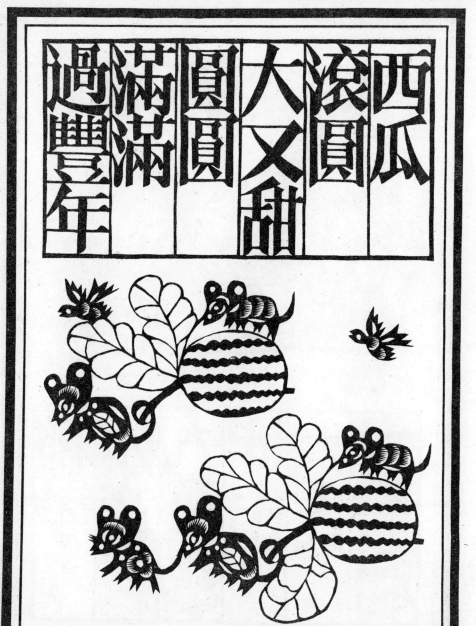

西瓜滚圆大又甜，
圆圆满满过丰年。

Xīguā gǔnyuán dà yòu tián,
yuányuán mǎnmǎn guò
fēngnián.

Watermelons are sweet and
large and than usual
plumper,
A sign that at each year's
harvest the crops will be
bumper.

59

柿子如意大公鸡，
开市大吉求吉利。

Shìzi rúyì dà gōngjī,
kāishì dàjí qiú jílì.

Both sweet persimmons and
a large crowing cock
Are auspicious objects for
the opening of a new shop.

喜酒喜糖多带点，
婆家亲友都分遍。

Xǐjiǔ xǐtáng duō dàidiǎnr,
pójia qīnyǒu dōu fēnbiàn.

The bride's family takes along sweets and wine for wedding libations,
To be distributed among the groom's friends and relations.

小车送礼真带劲，
一路小跑不喊累。

Xiǎochē sònglǐ zhēn dàijìnr,
yílù xiǎopǎo bù hǎn lèi.

Small carts for carrying gifts
   are good and strong.
Smoothly and steadily they
   move along.

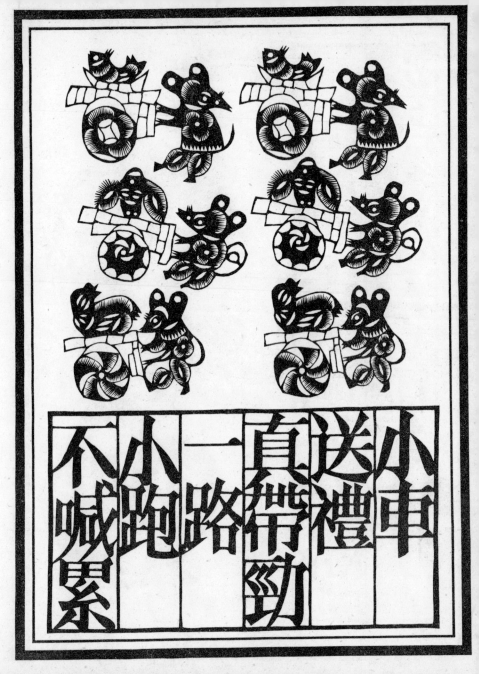

前面送的是嫁妆，
后面来的是傧相。

Qiánmian sòng de shì
jiàzhuang,
hòumian lái de shì
bīnxiàng.

First comes the dowry for
    the bride,
Then the bridal attendants
    follow behind.

63

侯相都是娘家客，
前来送亲几百个。

Bīnxiàng dōu shì niángjia
kè,
qiánlái sòngqīn jǐbǎi gè.

The attendants are all from
the bride's family,
Whose guests number two
hundred—or even three.

64

外公去把喜酒吃，
外婆比它还着急。

Wàigōng qù bǎ xǐjiǔ chī,
wàipó bǐ tā hái zháojí.

Hastening to the wedding is
    old Grandpa,
And in an even greater hurry
    is Grandma.

父母二老打扮好，
酒席桌上少不了。

Fùmǔ èr lǎo dǎban hǎo,
jiǔxí zhuō shang shǎo bù
liǎo.

Mr. and Mrs. Mouse are
  both decked out,
On their way to the banquet
  they parade about.

66

七大姑和八大姨，
娘家亲戚要去齐。

Qī dàgū hé bā dàyí,
niángjia qīnqi yào qùqí.

Seventh Aunt and Eighth
  Aunt come along too.
Slighting any of the bride's
  relatives will not do.

67

二爷二奶和二嫂，
二叔二婶少不了。

Èryé èrnǎi hé èrsǎo,
èrshū èrshěn shǎo bu liǎo.

Then come Second Uncle,
Second Aunt and Second
Sister-in-Law.
Great Uncles and Great
Aunts show up all.

大哥大嫂齐叫到，
表兄表妹不能少。

Dàgē dàsǎo qí jiàodào,
biǎoxiōng biǎomèi bùnéng
shǎo.

Also attending are Eldest
　　Brother and Sister-in-Law,
And all the bride's cousins,
　　large and small.

69

大舅二舅和小舅，
还有孩子一大溜。

Dàjiù èrjiù hé xiǎojiù,
háiyǒu háizi yídàliù.

Eldest, Second and Youngest
Uncle are invited also.
Together with a big troop of
children to the wedding
feast they go.

70

娘家贵客这么多，
交通运输真罗嗦。

Niángjia guìkè zhème duō,
jiāotōng   yùnshū   zhēn
luōsuo.

Of so many members is the
bride's family composed
That in finding transporta-
tion a big problem is
posed.

大车拉，小车载，
还是不好来安排。

Dàchē lā xiǎochē zài,
háishi bùhǎo lái ānpái.

Large carts and small carts
the bride's relations fill,
But transporting them all is a
difficult matter still.

只好按资来排位，
不能得罪老长辈。

Zhǐhǎo ànzī lái páiwèi,
bùnéng dézuì lǎo zhǎngbèi.

The places in the carts are
    arranged by seniority, for
    sure,
For no one wants their elders
    any hardships to endure.

外公坐车坐不牢，
找只花鞋当花轿。

Wàigāng zuò chē zuò bu
láo,
zhǎo zhī huāxié dàng
huājiào.

Sitting in a cart Grandpa
   cannot bear,
So he finds a suitable shoe to
   use as a sedan chair.

74

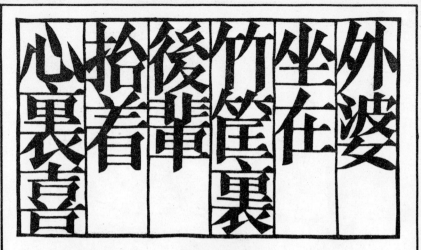

外婆坐在竹筐里，
后辈抬着心里喜。

Wàipó zuòzài zhúlán li,
hòubèi táizhe xīn li xǐ.

Comfortably Grandma sits
in a basket of bamboo,
Delighted that the young-
sters are carrying her
through.

75

双套马车向前奔，
父母二人笑开颜。

Shuāngtào mǎchē xiàngqián bèn,
fùmǔ èr rén xiào kāiyán.

A two-horse carriage hastens ahead,
With Mr. and Mrs. Mouse beaming to see their daughter wed.

单套马车跑得急，
三爷四奶坐一起。

Dāntào mǎchē pǎo de jí,
sānyé sìnǎi zuò yìqǐ.

And the one-horse carriage
goes at quite a clip,
On it Third Great Uncle and
Fourth Great Aunt sit.

77

小驴车，快加鞭，
五叔六婶坐里边。

Xiǎolúchē, kuài jiā biān,
wǔshū liùshěnr zuò lǐbian.

Giddyap, above the mule cart
cracks the whip.
Inside, on a bench Fifth Uncle and Sixth Aunt sit.

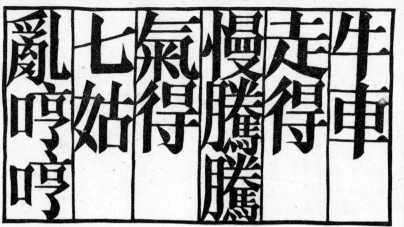

牛车走得慢腾腾，
气得七姑乱哼哼。

Niúchē　　　zǒu　　　de
màntēngtēng,
qì de qīgū luànhēngheng.

And the cart drawn by an ox
　so slowly sways
That impatient Seventh Aunt
　curses all the way.

79

八大姨，徒步行，
边走边喊小外甥。

Bā dàyí, túbù xíng,
biān zǒu biān hǎn xiǎo
wàisheng.

Eighth Aunt on foot comes
  along,
Calling out for her nephews
  as she trudges on.

八大姨徒步行

邊走邊喊小外甥

80

大哥大嫂走得急，
拖家带口不容易。

Dàgē dàsǎo zǒu de jí,
tuō jiā dài kǒu bù róngyi.

Moving the entire family is
  not an easy matter.
Eldest brother and his wife
  along the way clatter.

表兄表妹手拉手，
兄弟姐妹一起走。

Biǎoxiōng biǎomèi shǒu lā
shǒu,
xiōngdì jiěmèi yìqǐ zǒu.

Hand in hand cousins stride,
And brothers and sisters
    walk side by side.

82

后面还有小娃娃，
边跑边喊叫妈妈。

Hòumian　　háiyou　　xiǎo
wáwa，
biān　pǎo　biān　hǎn　jiào
māma.

One small child is tagging behind,
Calling for her Mother as
her way she tries to find.

83

有的娃娃饿得慌，
妈妈喂奶坐路旁。

Yǒu de wáwa è de huāng,
māma wèi nǎi zuò lù páng.

Some babies are too hungry
    to wait,
So by the roadside their
    mothers their hunger must
    sate.

84

有的娃娃真顽皮，
妈妈只好用绳系。

Yǒu de wáwa zhēng wánpí,
māma zhǐhǎo yòng shéng jì.

Because one small child is more mischievous than most,
His mother has to tie him up with a rope.

有的娃娃很省心，
手拉玩具后边跟。

Yǒu de wáwa hěn shěngxīn,
shǒu lā wánjù hòubian gēn.

A well-behaved child (his
  mother he minds)
With a string pulls a toy that
  drags behind.

86

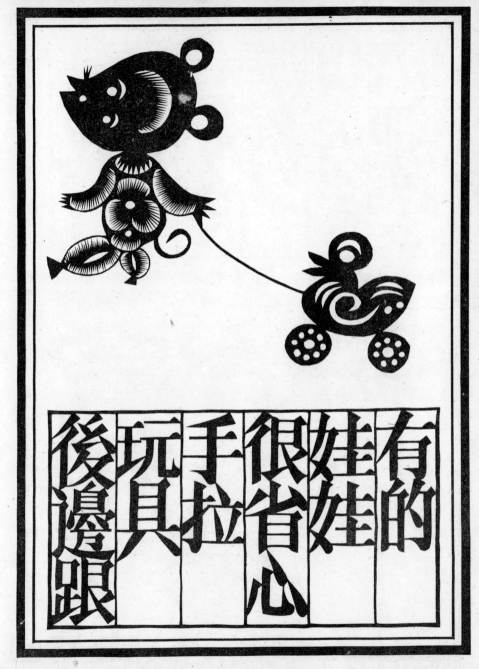

娘家客人都走尽，
鼠官后面来压阵。

Niángjia kèren dōu zǒujìn,
shǔguān hòumian lái yāzhèn.

The bride's family proceeds
with all its gear,
And the Mice officials bring
up the rear.

跨过山梁走小桥，
猫咪新房马上到。

Kuàguo shānliáng zǒu
xiǎoqiáo,
māomī xīnfáng mǎshàng
dào.

After crossing mountain
ridges and then small
bridges, they arrive at the
Cat's house,
Where the bridal chamber
has been prepared for
Miss Mouse.

猫咪新房马上到
跨过山梁走小桥

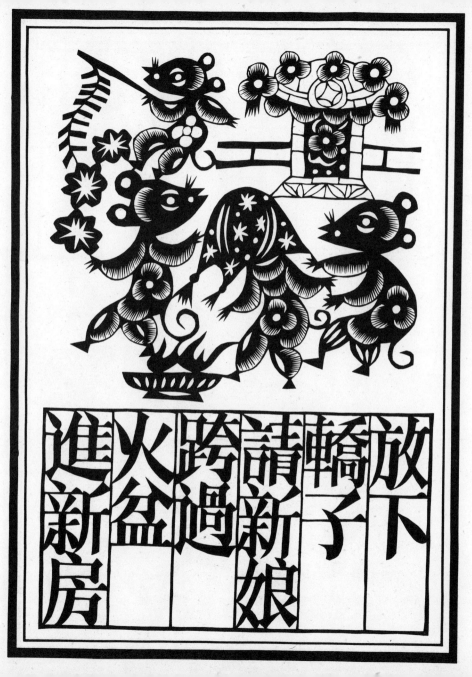

放下轿子请新娘，
跨过火盆进新房。

Fàngxia jiàozi qǐng xīnniáng,
kuàguo huǒpén jìn xīnfáng.

The sedan chair is lowered to the ground.
Custom demands the bride a brazier step over and around.

拜完天地拜高堂，
拜完高堂拜新郎。

Bàiwán tiāndì bài gāotáng,
bàiwán gāotáng bài
xīnláng.

Bowing to Heaven and
Earth before entering the
groom's house,
The bride bows to the
groom's parents and then
to her spouse.

90

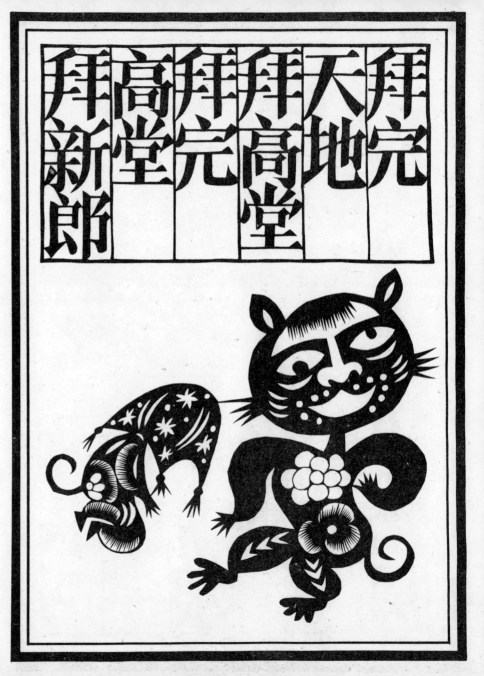

猫咪美得笑声响，
牵着新娘入洞房。

Māomī měi de xiàoshēng xiǎng,
qiānzhe xīnniáng rù dòngfáng.

The Cat is grinning from ear
　　to ear,
As into the wedding chamber
　　Miss Mouse he steers.

挑开新娘红头巾，
猫把新娘肚里吞。

Tiǎokāi xīnniáng hóng
tóujīn,
māo bǎ xīnniáng dù li tūn.

The Cat pulls away the red
scarf covering her head,
And swallows his bride
whole before anything's
said.

92

吉庆佳日庆回门，
鼠爸鼠妈来串亲。

Jíqìng jiārì qìng huímén,
shǔbà shǔmā lái chuànqīn.

The happy day when the
    bride is to visit her Dad
    and Mum,
Mr. and Mrs. Mouse to their
    daughter's new house
    come.

93

二老走进新洞房，
不见女儿来喊娘。

Èrlǎo zǒujìn xīn dòngfáng,
bújiàn nǚ'er lái hǎn niáng.

Her parents enter Miss
  Mouse's room,
And call out for her, but she
  doesn't seem to be home.

二老等得心着急，
大喊女儿在那里。

Èrlǎo děng de xīn zháojí,
dà hǎn nǚ'er zài nǎlǐ.

A long time the parents im-
   patiently wait and shout
For their dear daughter,
   Miss Mouse, to come out.

猫咪见到二老急，
赶忙出来作解释。

Māomī jiàndao èrlǎo jí,
gǎnmáng chūlai zuò jiěshi.

Seeing that Mr. and Mrs.
  Mouse are really upset,
The Cat emerges, and an ex-
  planation they get.

96

猫说爱妻怕人欺，
为保安全吞肚里。

Māo shuō àiqī pà rén qī,
wèi bǎo ānquán tūn dù li.

"To put my loving wife in
    complete safety,
I have swallowed her into my
    stomach," says he.

老鼠父母听此言，
吓得逃命不迟延。

Lǎoshǔ fùmǔ tīng cǐyán,
xià de táomìng bù chíyán.

Scared out of their wits Mr.
  and Mrs. Mouse are,
So they take to their heels
  and, fast as they can, run
  afar.

98

父母二老真伤心，
嫁女不该攀高亲。

Fùmǔ èrlǎo zhēn shāngxīn,
jià nǔ bù gāi pān gāojīn.

Mr. and Mrs. Mouse are full
   of remorse,
Regretting that in choosing a
   spouse for their daughter
   they took such a course.

攀高親　不該　嫁女　真傷心　二老　父母

老鼠嫁女成笑话，
笑话传遍千万家。

Lǎoshǔ jià nǔ chéng
xiàohua,
xiàohua chuánbiàn qiānwàn
jiā.

By marrying off their daughter to a Cat,
Mr. and Mrs. Mouse by all
are laughed at.

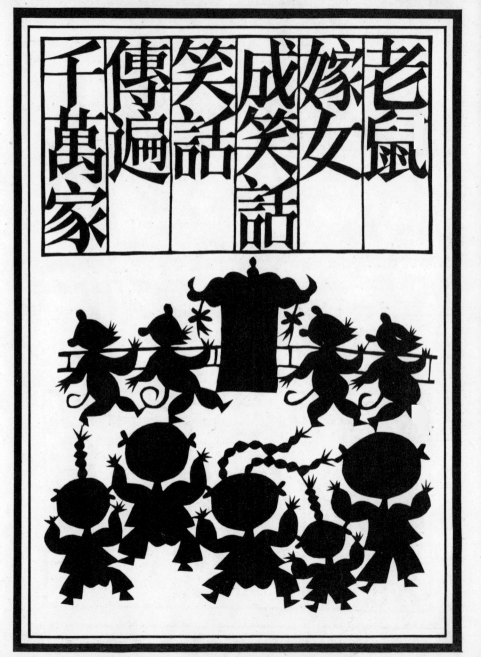

（京）新登 134 号
责任编辑　蔡希勤
封面设计　于　平　任　凭

老鼠嫁女
于平　任凭

*
华语教学出版社出版
（中国北京百万庄路 24 号）
邮政编码 100037
北京外文印刷厂印刷
中国国际图书贸易总公司发行
（中国北京车公庄西路 35 号）
北京邮政信箱第 399 号　邮政编码 100044
1993 年（20 开）第一版
（汉英）
ISBN 7－80052－257－1/J·1120（外）
01800
88－CE－466p